Easy FILM Tunes for Clarinet

With Piano Accompaniment

Arranged by Stephen Duro

CW00417833

Chester Music
(A division of Music Sales Limited)
8/9 Frith Street
London W1V 5TZ

This book © Copyright 1999 Chester Music
Order No. CH61469 ISBN 0-7119-6989-2

Music processed by Allegro Reproductions
Cover design by Ian Butterworth
Cover photograph by Ron Sutherland
Printed in the United Kingdom by
Caligraving Limited, Thetford, Norfolk

CD orchestrations and production by Paul Honey
Solo clarinet: John Whelan

Contents

A TIME FOR US
Love Theme from 'Romeo And Juliet'

Music by Nino Rota
Words by Eddie Snyder and Larry Kusik

Slow and expressive

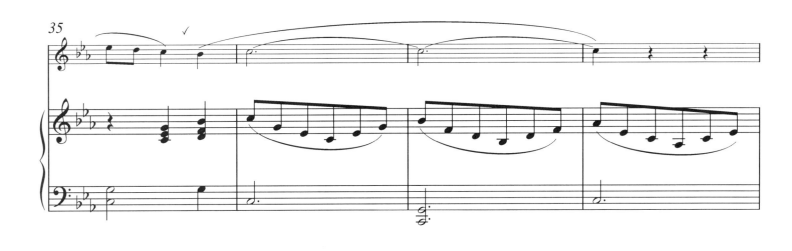

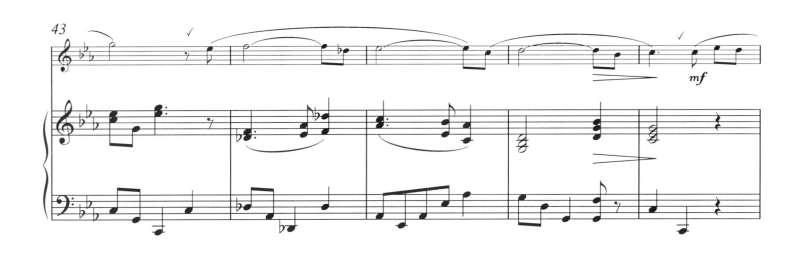

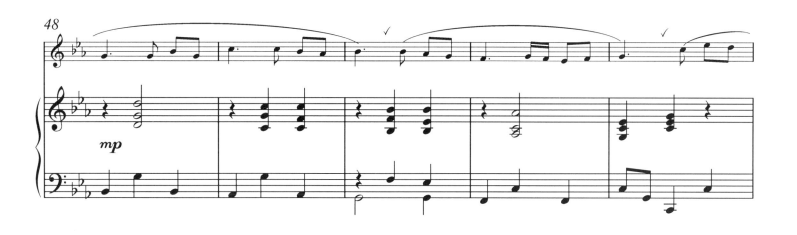

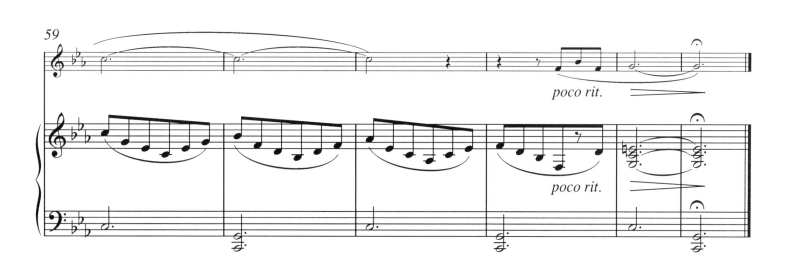

CAN YOU FEEL THE LOVE TONIGHT?
From Walt Disney Pictures' 'The Lion King'

Music by Elton John
Words by Tim Rice

Moderately

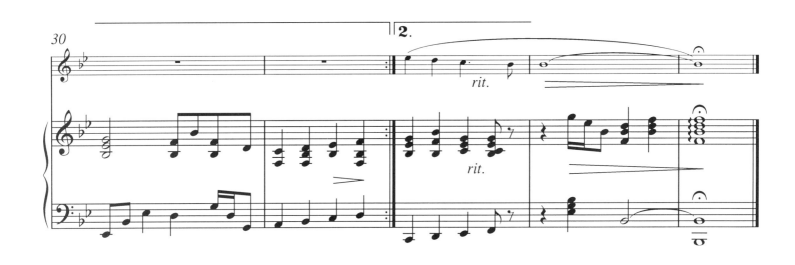

CIRCLE OF LIFE
From Walt Disney Pictures' 'The Lion King'

Music by Elton John
Words by Tim Rice

Moderately

COLORS OF THE WIND
From Walt Disney Pictures' 'Pocahontas'

Music by Alan Menken
Words by Stephen Schwartz

Moderately

EVERYBODY'S TALKIN'
From 'Midnight Cowboy'

Words and music by Fred Neil

Moderately

Easy FILM Tunes for Clarinet

Clarinet part

Arranged by Stephen Duro

Chester Music
(A division of Music Sales Limited)
8/9 Frith Street
London W1V 5TZ

Contents

A TIME FOR US

Love Theme from 'Romeo And Juliet'

Music by Nino Rota
Words by Eddie Snyder and Larry Kusik

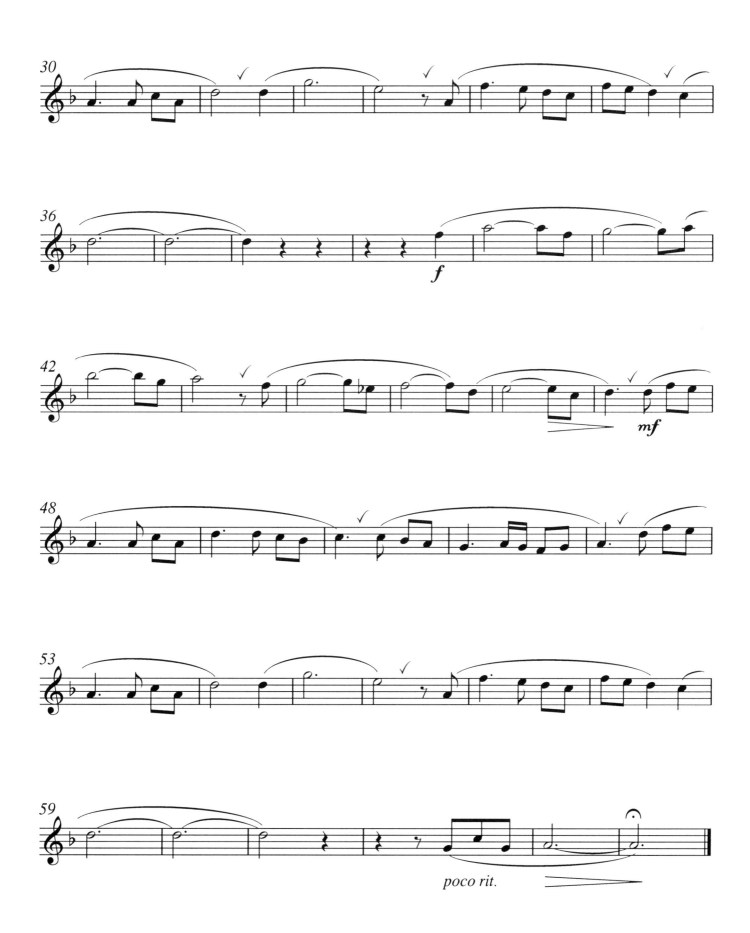

CAN YOU FEEL THE LOVE TONIGHT?

From Walt Disney Pictures' 'The Lion King'

Music by Elton John
Words by Tim Rice

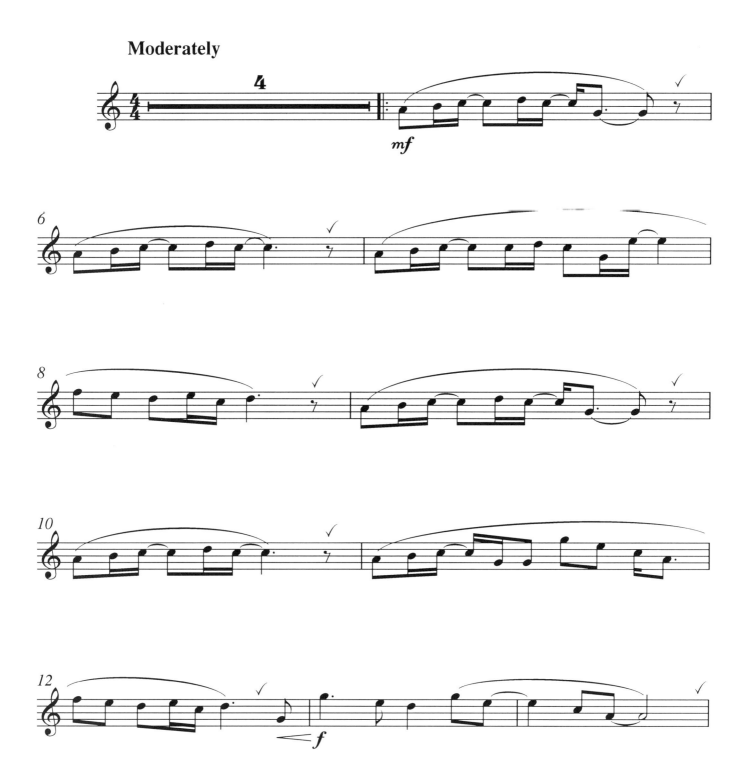

CIRCLE OF LIFE

From Walt Disney Pictures' 'The Lion King'

Music by Elton John
Words by Tim Rice

poco rit.

meno mosso   ***mp***

COLORS OF THE WIND

From Walt Disney Pictures' 'Pocahontas'

Music by Alan Menken
Words by Stephen Schwartz

D.S. al Coda   CODA

EVERYBODY'S TALKIN'

From 'Midnight Cowboy'

Words and music by Fred Neil

poco cresc.

mp

13

TRY A LITTLE TENDERNESS

from 'The Commitments'

Words and music by Harry Woods, Jimmy Campbell and Reg Connelly

HOW DEEP IS YOUR LOVE

From 'Saturday Night Fever'

Words and music by Barry Gibb, Robin Gibb and Maurice Gibb

MOON RIVER

From 'Breakfast At Tiffany's'

Music by Henry Mancini
Words by Johnny Mercer

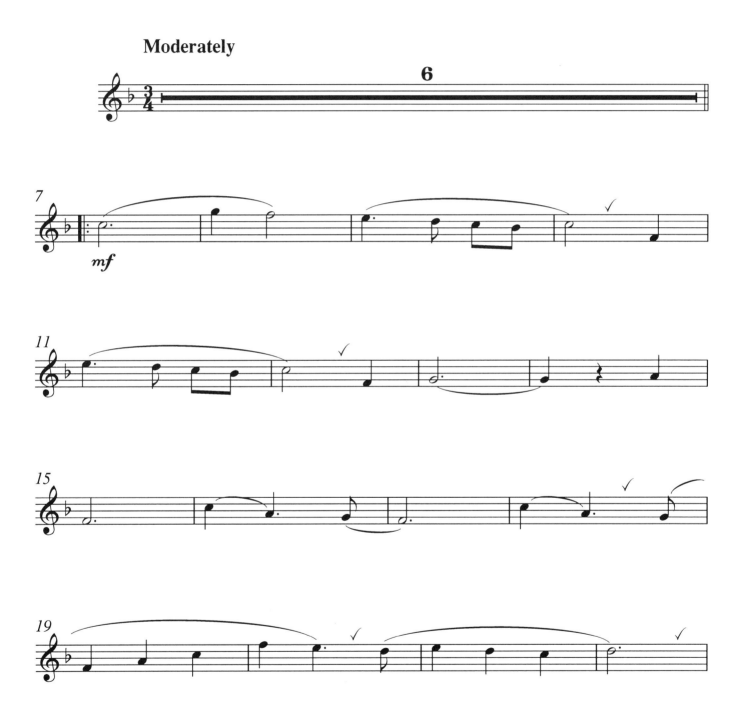

19

THE ENTERTAINER

From 'The Sting'

By Scott Joplin

Moderate ragtime

THE RAIDERS MARCH

From 'Raiders Of The Lost Ark'

By John Williams

TRY A LITTLE TENDERNESS
from 'The Commitments'

Words and music by Harry Woods, Jimmy Campbell & Reg Connelly

Moderately

HOW DEEP IS YOUR LOVE

From 'Saturday Night Fever'

Words and music by Barry Gibb, Robin Gibb and Maurice Gibb

Moderate ballad style

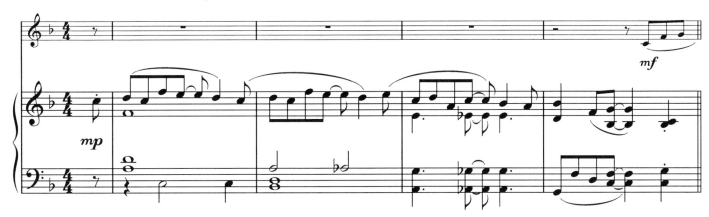

MOON RIVER
From 'Breakfast At Tiffany's'

Music by Henry Mancini
Words by Johnny Mercer

Moderately

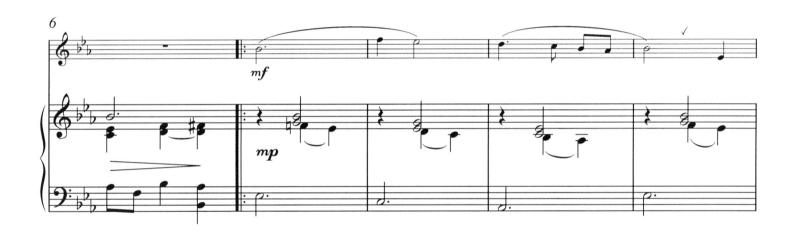

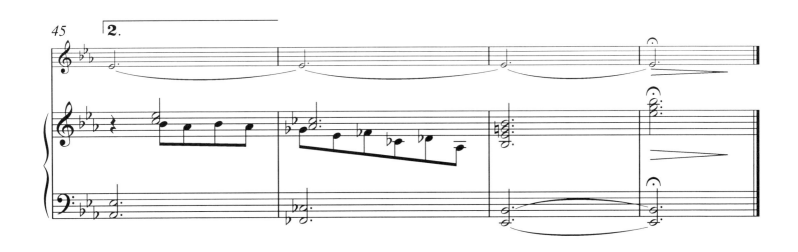

THE ENTERTAINER
From 'The Sting'

By Scott Joplin

Moderate ragtime

THE RAIDERS MARCH
From 'Raiders Of The Lost Ark'

By John Williams

With movement

36